LFA Health

CW01020901

T'ai Chi S\

Movements 1 – 108

Explained in an easy to follow format

By Sheila Dickinson
President of the LFA Health Arts

Benefits:-
Helps to improve balance and co-ordination
Helps to improve joint mobility
Eases Stress
Provides Relaxation

Printed and published in Great Britain by

STAIRWAY
DISTRIBUTION
LTD.

P 0 BOX 19,
HEDON,
HULL
HU12 8YR

First Published 2003

Published by Stairway Distribution Limited
PO Box 19, Hedon. Hull. HU12 8YR
www.leefamilyarts.com

Please consult your Doctor before taking part in the following exercise programme.
The LFA and Stairway Distribution Ltd disclaim any liability for loss or injury in connection with the advice and exercises included in this book.

Acknowledgements

To the past Masters of our Arts - we offer our sincere
thanks!

THE LFA T'AI CHI LIBRARY

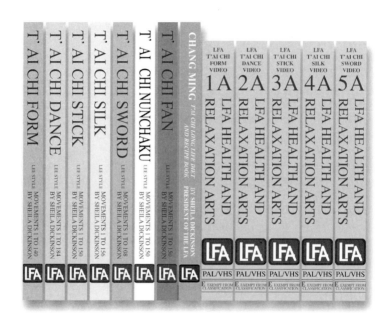

All of the above Books and Videos are available from:-
Stairway Distribution Limited
PO Box 19
Hedon
HU12 8YR
Tel/Fax 01482 896063

You may also order from our Websites, please visit:
www.leefamilyarts.com   www.lfataichi.com

CONTENTS

Foreword

Welcome to the Lee Family Arts T'ai Chi Sword Set. Please note, I have used the same foreword in each of my books in order that I can pay tribute to my late Grand Master, Chee Soo.

My position as President of the Lee Family Arts started in January 1995. Since that time, I have had the privilege to guide my fellow instructors in all aspects of LFA T'ai Chi, and I have worked hard to reach as many people as possible, so that everyone may gain from the many health benefits of our Arts.

I would not be writing this book today without the guidance and patience of my late Grand Master Chee Soo, who spent most of his life teaching the Lee Family Arts. Chee Soo is in my thoughts constantly and I offer my sincere thanks for receiving the benefit of his wisdom and understanding.

Chee Soo wrote five books published by the Aquarian Press, sadly at the time of writing only one title remains in print today 'The Chinese Art of T'ai Chi Ch'uan'. In this book he traces the history of the Lee Style back to Ho-Hsieh Lee circa 1,000BC. It is stated that the Lee Family have always been Taoists and that the Lee Style is a Yin and Yang style, this means that everything within it is in complete balance and harmony.

Chee Soo occasionally spoke of his own Grand Master, Chan Kam Lee and told of how they had met during 1934 in Hyde Park in London. In those days there were very few Oriental people in London and the two became friends. It was a friendship that would change Chee Soo's life forever. After Chan Kam Lee's death, Chee Soo dedicated himself to maintaining the knowledge and wisdom he had learnt from Chan Kam Lee.

While staying with my family and my self, Chee Soo talked to me about the future of the Lee Family Arts and the direction he wished them to take. On Monday the 16th May 1994 Chee Soo asked me to give him my word that I would not let the Lee Family Arts die.

Sadly, Chee Soo died on the 29th August 1994.

It is with the greatest respect to Chee Soo that I offer my own writings and understanding of the lessons he taught me.

The names of the Instructors who have trained, qualified and still maintain their own training can be obtained from the Lee Family Arts official register of qualified instructors. The LFA can only vouch for the quality and content of that which is taught within an official LFA registered class.

The Lee Family Arts have been tried and tested for thousands of years before we were born. The people who teach them are merely caretakers, who have the privilege of maintaining the Arts, and witnessing them helping others. This book teaches you the first one hundred and eight movements of the LFA T'ai Chi Sword and also gives valuable additional information on special exercises used within our Arts (see below). There are a total of two hundred and sixteen movements in our Sword set and these latter movements will be explained in further publications.

Please note that in addition to teaching the first 108 movements of the T'ai Chi Sword set, I have included sections covering The T'ai Chi Long Life Diet (called Chang Ming); Why LFA T'ai Chi? What is the Way of Occlusion? The Warm Up. The reason for including this information in this volume (as opposed to say in the LFA T'ai Chi Form book), is to broaden the information available to everyone who have given their valuable time and practised the movements shown in our T'ai Chi Form, Dance, Stick and Silk books. This is an example of how your journey with the LFA, will always be fruitful.

The Lee Family Arts will always be known as a Family Art and it is a family which grows in numbers daily. In concluding, I would like to say a very special welcome to you!

A Natural Way of Life

To define a natural way of life is not an easy thing to do in this day and age. Life moves at a much faster pace than it did when the Lee Family Arts was first developed in China. The modern day world is full of distractions, our food, as well as many other aspects of our lives are packaged and marketed to tempt us to indulge in quick fix enjoyment to satisfy our needs.

Yet is a quick fix the answer to a lifetime of good health? In our world of rushing around trying to do everything yesterday, what about you, your body deserves the very best. To achieve the best performance from your car, you feed it the appropriate fuel and have it regularly serviced and maintained to avoid major defects as it grows older. This preventative maintenance avoids small situations becoming large problems. Doesn't it make sense to do the same for your own body? I have witnessed people ask my late Master's advice on health related matters. Before any recommendation he always asked one question 'Are you on the diet?' The diet he referred to was the Chang Ming T'ai Chi Long Life Diet. In other words, he knew that you had to be ready to help yourself. We all truthfully know if we are eating healthily. It is without exception that if we are in charge of our faculties, nothing passes our lips without our agreement. I have heard it argued: - 'but I have to eat what my wife cooks,' - your agreement.

'I just couldn't resist that bar of chocolate,' - your agreement.

'I haven't the time,' - your agreement.

When I first started the Chang Ming Diet, our three children were quite young, I tried to tempt them to eat the Chang Ming way. They didn't want to, so I tried to cook them a healthy alternative and then cook Chang Ming food for my husband and myself.

The temptations and the excuses to avoid healthy eating are endless; I know because I have used some of them myself.

It is unfortunate that it often takes life-threatening circumstances before we evaluate what is important. *Let's face it, without life, the rest is irrelevant.* In Chee Soo's book 'The Tao of Long Life' Chee wishes everyone well - whichever path they choose and hopes their suffering will not be too painful. I have to admit when I first read this I thought it was a little harsh. After studying the Lee Family Arts for many years, I understand that we all have personal choices. The Tao of Long Life was the very first of Chee's books that I read; this was a year before I started training with Chee Soo.

I remember reading his book and thinking well, I could follow that diet but why would I want to. A year later I started on the Chang Ming Diet, Chee used to say 'we all usually receive approximately one years' warning'. If there is a significant change in your life, look back, the signs, of its coming were there even if you didn't recognise them.

Another thing Chee advised me to do was keep a journal. When we are busy leading our lives, we do not always realise how far we have travelled and how thankful we should be. The last words my late Master spoke to me were 'Have a safe journey Sheila.' Yet a journey is more than the distance covered between towns or countries; a journey lasts for much longer throughout your lifetime and beyond.

At first sight the Chang Ming Diet is not an easy diet to follow, yet with a little practise you can find recipes to replace your old favourites. *To help everyone enjoy the Chang Ming diet, I have published a Chang Ming Long Life Diet and Recipe Book which also gives information on all aspects of our Arts.*

The above publication is entitled Chang Ming – T'ai Chi Long Life Diet and Recipe Book and is available from Stairway Distribution Limited who publish all of my books.

Listed below are the foods which are included in the Chang Ming Diet. You will find that it is not a vegetarian diet, although I personally am a vegetarian and simply adapt the diet to suit my needs.

There will be people who are allergic to dairy produce, others who cannot eat wheat or nuts, the Chang Ming Diet can be adapted to help improve the quality of everyone's health.

Foods which are Allowed

1/ Anything made from natural whole grain, which has not been refined, e.g. brown rice, buckwheat, maize, barley, rye, soya, these are sometimes found in breakfast cereals and are excellent in cakes and bread.

2/ All root vegetables EXCEPT potatoes, tomatoes, peppers, aubergines, rhubarb, and spinach, which are NOT to be eaten. The first three are related to the deadly nightshade family and contain glycoalkaloids which are poisonous to a high proportion of human beings.

3/ Bean sprouts - all varieties.

4/ Kidney beans, haricot beans, butter beans, chickpeas.

5/ Seaweed.

6/ Locally grown fruits and berries (in moderation).

7/ Nuts (unsalted).

8/ Low fat natural yoghurt.

9/ Honey.

10/ Cottage cheese or vegetarian cheese.

11/ Herb teas and China teas.

12/ Vegetable margarine/oils

13/ Eggs (scrambled or in omelettes) or eat the yolks only.

14/ Natural sea salt, soya sauce, sesame seed salt.

15/ All dried fruits, cherries, raisins, apricots etc.

16/ Wild vegetables and herbs

17/ All grain milks, rice milk, coconut milk, soya milk.

18/ Fruit drinks made from locally grown fruit.

19/ Vegetarian meat (check the labels).

The following may also be used if necessary

20/ Non fat fish excluding those from the list of foods which are not allowed.

21/ Sea food – shrimps, prawns etc. (Please be wary of crabmeat).

20/ Wild Birds – pheasant, pigeon etc.

21/ Wild or free range chicken, turkey etc.

22/ Skimmed milk or powdered skimmed milk.

Foods which are Not Allowed

1/ Refined and processed foods (if colourings, preservatives, flavourings, or other chemicals are included, do not eat them).

2/ Any grain foods which have been processed.

3/ All deep fried foods.

4/ Coffee, alcohol, tobacco, chocolate and other sweets.

5/ Spices, rock salt, mustard, pepper, vinegar, pickles, curry, chilli.

6/ Meat, pork, beef, mutton, and lamb.

7/ Salmon, mackerel, shark, swordfish, tuna and whale.

8/ Sugar, ice cream, jellies, synthetic fruit juices.

9/ Potatoes, tomatoes, aubergines, peppers, rhubarb, spinach.

10/ Concentrated meat extracts, meat soups and meat gravies.

11/ Milk, boiled or fried eggs.

12/ Lard or dripping which comes from animal fats.

13/ Any bird or fish which has a lot of fat tissue.

14/ [Allowed in moderation] Low fat cheese, yoghurt.

Chee Soo explained that on average the Chinese eat only twice a day, this gives the body enough time to digest the food from one meal and allow it to distribute the nutrients around the system before the next intake of food.

In all of Chee Soo's books the importance of the Chang Ming diet to the individual is emphasised. A complete book of recipes and information about the Chang Ming diet has been written by myself and published by Stairway Distribution Limited.

You may think that it is strange to include an introduction to a special diet within our LFA T'ai Chi Sword book. The reason for this is to inform students who have steadily progressed through the T'ai Chi Form, Dance, Stick and Silk, of the many extra benefits and additional energies which are there for everyone. By using the

Diet to cleanse the body of toxins which have accumulated over a lifetime, you will be better placed to live a healthier life in this fast living day and age.

Why LFA T'ai Chi?

Over the years I have been asked many times 'why LFA T'ai Chi' The easy answer to this is – 'it works'. From the very beginning of your training you are able to experience the feel good factor. In my classes I explain that if the body is tense it cannot work properly. Your body's own natural energy (chi) cannot circulate easily when you are tense, this in turn can result in the onset of poor health.

If we are having a good time and enjoying life, time flies by. However, if people are fed up with their lot, time drags and we can see no way forward.

LFA T'ai Chi helps to introduce balance into our lives, it does not matter whether we understand it or not. The gentle movements work; quite often it is our friends and family who notice the change in us. Recently a lady came to one of my classes to see exactly why LFA T'ai Chi had changed her friend's life so dramatically. Her friend had gone from being a highly stressed individual who constantly complained about been tired, and the injustices which life threw at her, to being a happy energetic individual with a zest for life and all it has to offer. How many times do we hear people joke 'if I could bottle it I would make a fortune'. We do not have to bottle LFA T'ai Chi, it is available to everyone via one or more of our many classes, day courses, summer schools, videos and books. What we are offering is more than the feel good factor, we are teaching an ancient Art which will help to improve the quality of your health. The importance of exercise is constantly emphasised by the medical profession. Practising LFA T'ai Chi offers you so much more than exercise. We teach you how to help yourself to heal your body. For those who are over weight, we offer toning exercises and we are able to recommend an eating programme. The LFA can teach you how to use herbal compresses for certain ailments, for example an onion poultice, is an excellent way to alleviate a cold. A ginger compress can help arthritic joints. A cabbage leaf can be used to reduce swelling.

Some styles of T'ai Chi teach the movements as a martial art, the importance of the movements for your health may also be mentioned. The Lee Family have always taught the T'ai Chi purely for health, for without good health we have nothing. For people wishing to learn a self-defence art, the Lee Family offers the art of Feng Shou. Feng Shou is more physically demanding than LFA T'ai Chi. Personally I recommend that if you are interested in learning the Art of Feng Shou, you should first ensure your body is healthy by practising LFA T'ai Chi.

A lot of modern day classes can only take students to a certain level of understanding. With the LFA, there is no limit to what we are able to teach you. The LFA is there to guide you every step of the way. First you will learn the mechanics, then how to apply the correct breathing. Another step is to learn the connection between the energy centres. A true teacher will guide you, without putting the ideas into your head. LFA T'ai Chi is a journey of discovery. It contains no short cuts, as you reach the necessary level of understanding, the LFA and I will be there to guide you to the next level.

What is the Way of Occlusion?

Please note that in the LFA we say to our students that it is better to practise ten movements with depth and understanding, rather than one hundred and forty movements not so well. Likewise with the following, if you only achieve a small percentage of understanding, then you will have gained immensely.

The Way of Occlusion is fully explained in 'The Taoist Ways of Healing' by the Grand Master, Chee Soo. In this book I offer my own understanding of his wisdom.

Although many people, both Eastern and Western may have heard of the way of occlusion, (some may even have spent a great deal of time studying the subject), to most it still remains a great mystery. Only people who practise the Lee Family Arts and make them their way of life, can begin to appreciate the way of occlusion and even then it takes many, many years to achieve this level of understanding for this is a very advanced level indeed.

The Lee Family Arts are based on many different types of energies which exist within the body (if you are truly healthy). From the moment you were born certain energies came into being. If you have developed correctly during the stages of growing up and added to these energies by correct eating habits, then you are on the correct path to occlusion.

The energies comprise of five sections physical, mental, internal, external, and spiritual; each section must be fully mastered before we fully understand The Way of Occlusion.

PHYSICAL DEVELOPMENT

We use our physical body whether at work, rest or play. I was taught that great physical strength is not a sign of great physical energy. In fact the opposite applies, for large muscles may restrict growth and restrict the flow of blood which in turn encourages water retention. It is possible for some organs to swell while others contract, diminishing the potential of physical vitality.

It is in this section of his book that Chee Soo once again states the importance of being on the Chang Ming diet.

He explains that only by eating the Chang Ming way can we hope to attain good health.

MENTAL ENERGY (chingshen)

This area has been covered in a vast variety of books and in recent years many books have come onto the market regarding the power of positive thought and the difference between the conscious and the subconscious mind. The Ancient Taoist understood this concept knowing how important it was to have complete relaxation of the mind, body and spirit for the retention of good health. Mental energy is used for the process of thinking, controlling the movement of our limbs, counteracting stresses and strains (the latter can add an emotional drain to our lives). It is also used for intuition, sensory perception, hypersensitivity and of course Taoist Wand and Taoist Meditation.

Mental energy is also used to control, channel and harness all the other vitalities within the body - whether you are awake or asleep.

INTERNAL ENERGY (chi)

Scientists have become aware of various energies within the universe for example electricity, magnetism, gravity etc. Who is to say that there aren't other energies to become aware of? During the past 3000 years, the Chinese became aware of several energies e.g. Chi energy and Li energy. It is amazing that they have been able to keep this information secret for so long. The Lee family Arts came out of China in the nineteen thirties especially to benefit people in the West, thus the balance of yin and yang, East and West is achieved. Do we really want to ignore this fact?

The benefits of chi energy to your health are beyond normal comprehension. Everyone practising the Lee Family Arts works at activating this energy for the good health of their mind, body and spirit. When harnessed, it can be a far greater force than sheer physical strength. It is amazing that although we are all born with it, most people allow their chi to lie dormant within them. Your chi energy came into being when you where inside your mother and will not leave you until you take your last breath. In the early days of our life we automatically use our chi energy, however by the time we reach the age of five or six, our physical energy takes over and our chi is left to lie dormant. Only when you have passed through all the stages of practising LFA T'ai Chi will you be able to obtain the dynamic benefits of this energy. The rewards are constant good health, peace of mind, happiness and longevity.

First of all we have to learn how to relax the mind, body and spirit. This does not mean flopping into a chair, trying this kind of relaxation merely robs the body of its natural energy allowing it to seep away, and in turn the body can become lazy. Within the LFA, we use the time when the body is relaxed to store energy, the secret is to be able to relax at will whether at work, rest or play. It is important to strive to throw open the doors of relaxation both physically and mentally, so that there is not the slightest stress or strain. Eating a strictly Chang Ming Diet will greatly enhance the process. In addition, our breathing exercises should be incorporated into your daily life, this will help to speed up the process of making more energy, while at the same time helping you to relax even more.

Once you have learnt how to produce more energy and store it, the next stage is to learn how to move it around your body. Once again the LFA can provide special breathing exercises to help you direct the flow of your internal energy and develop the mental control over in which direction it moves. There is no set time scale for mastering these techniques, it depends purely on each individual's dedication to the task at hand.

To achieve full control of your internal energy is within the grasp of everyone, however it could take you five years or twenty years, in some cases people may train and never reach this level. It all depends on good eating and your dedication to your training. Another breathing exercise is introduced at this level to help you reach your quest, but only people who are ready will be able to fully use this exercise and benefit from its true potential. The LFA have the key, it is up to you to take it and unlock the door to your own personal development.

EXTERNAL ENERGY

Li energy is the external energy which ensures the order of the universe. It exists whether we believe in it or not. Li energy passes through everyone every moment of the day. In the LFA, we know it is necessary to build up and store both our internal energy and the external energy to ensure continuous good health. Chee Soo explained that a person who has built up both energies to the required level with never suffer from the dreaded illness of cancer that touches so many people's lives.

HEALING

Healing with energy does not require any special equipment, only the required energy levels plus an understanding of how the energy moves around the body. Not all instructors have reached this level of understanding. This type of healing should only be attempted by a very experienced teacher – with a mandate from their Master to wisely use this ability for the good of all.

MEDITATION

The Ancient Masters taught many different ways of meditating. Chee Soo explained that they could be separated into twenty basic and separate paths, yet each path may be divided into many subsections. If you are truly interested in learning to mediate using the way which has been handed down throughout the centuries, the LFA and I will teach you, the basics sound simple, the application takes dedication.

Taoist Walk

The Taoist walk is an extremely important part of the LFA health training because it moves the weight from

one leg to another in a special and subtle way. Not only is one leg working while the other one rests, but the working leg is the Yang leg and the resting leg is the Yin leg.

The weight is moved from one leg to the other before you try and alter the position of your foot.

Start with your feet slightly wider than shoulder width apart, toes pointing forwards. Both hands are held at waist height with the palms facing each other.

1/ Drift your weight across to your right side, your right knee bends, your hips and your bottom move across to the right side.

2/ Now take a very small step forwards with your left foot, placing your heel down first. Allow your left knee to bend, move your hips and bottom across to the left. Keep your right leg straight, do not lock your right knee.

Practise walking across the room in this manner. People suffering from back, hip, knee and ankle problems, reap great benefits from practising the Taoist Walk.

We use the Taoist Walk in all of our form sets. With practise it can be incorporated into your every day walk (so that it is undetectable), only you will know the benefits you are receiving each time you place one foot in front of the other.

The Taoist Walk helps to move your Chi energy into the lower part of your body. In the West we tend to carry a lot of energy congestion around the pelvic area, this stagnation leads to the above mentioned problems. So it is a good idea to learn to walk the Taoist Way.

Please try it for yourself, especially if you wake up in the morning feeling stiff, a few minutes practising the Taoist Walk could help to make you feel like a new man or woman.

Etiquette

The etiquette is something which has been handed down through the centuries along with the T'ai Chi, I  personally feel it represents a respect for the Arts we are practising and the ancient Masters to whom we owe so much.

When entering or leaving a training hall a student should bow to the room. This bow consists of bending forwards from the waist, at the same time, both palms rest on your thighs.

If you arrive after a class has already started you should walk round to the front of the hall, bow to the person taking the class and wait for them to bow to

you in return (using the bow explained below).

At the beginning of a class the bow consists of placing your right arm on top of your left in front of your body, your right hand palm faces down, and your left palm faces up.

When training with a partner you should both bow to each other at the start and finish (using the same bow as when entering and leaving the training room).

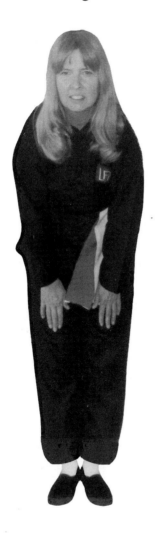

If an instructor offers you guidance with your training, you should bow to them after they have finished teaching you, (again using the bow for entering and leaving the training room).

The Warm Up

We use the following exercises at the beginning of all of our classes to gently move and exercise the body before we start our training session. There should be no strain when practising any of the LFA exercises.

Circling the Arms

Stand in Eagle stance.

1/ Start by circling your right arm forward (four complete circles).

2/ Change direction (four complete circles).

Repeat numbers one and two with the left arm.

EXTENSION

1/ Circle the right arm forwards and the left arm backwards (four complete circles).

2/ Circle the left arm forwards and the right arm backwards (four complete circles).

Swinging the Arms from Side to Side

Stand in Bear stance (feet shoulder width apart)
Swing both arms across to the right side of your body, and then to the left side of your body (four times on each side).

Keeping the Joints Mobile (Shoulders 1)

Stand in Eagle stance.

1/ Circle both shoulders forward.
Repeat three more times.
2/ Circle both shoulders backwards.
Repeat three more times.

Keeping the Joints Mobile (Shoulders 2)

Stand in Eagle stance.

1/ Circle one shoulder forwards and one shoulder backwards. Repeat three times.
2/ Change direction. Repeat three times.

Circling the Head

Stand in Bear stance (feet shoulder width apart)

1/ Keeping your teeth together, circle your head down and to the right, then up and round making one complete circle.

2/ Repeat in the opposite direction.

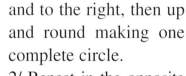

Moving Your Head from Side to Side

Stand in Bear stance (feet shoulder width apart)

1/ Turn your head to the right, then back to the centre.

2/ Turn your head to the left, then back to the centre.

Repeat three more times in each direction.

Moving your Head Backwards and Forwards

Stand in Bear stance (feet shoulder width apart)

1/ Lower your chin to your chest, then raise your head returning to the starting position.

2/ Tilt your head backwards, then straighten your head returning to the starting position.

Repeat both of the above movements three more times.

Lowering Your Weight

Stand in Bear stance (feet shoulder width apart).

1/ Place both hands together in front of your chest (palms facing each other, fingertips pointing to the ceiling).

2/ Breathe in through the nose as you bend your knees and lower your weight as far as possible.

3/ Breathe out through the mouth as you straighten your body.

Repeat movements two and three, once more.

Circling Your Hips

Stand in Bear stance (feet shoulder width apart).

1/ Place your hands on your hips and circle your hips

forwards and to your right, then to the rear and round to the left, then circle them round to the front (four times). Repeat, circling your hips to the left.

Leopard (warm up exercise)

Stand in Right Leopard stance (right leg bent, left leg straight).

1/ Move your right arm over the top of your head and lower your left hand down towards your left knee (three times).

2/ Change to Left Leopard stance, moving your left arm over the top of your head and lowering your right hand down towards your right knee (three times).

Chicken (warm up exercise)

Stand in Bear stance (feet shoulder width apart).

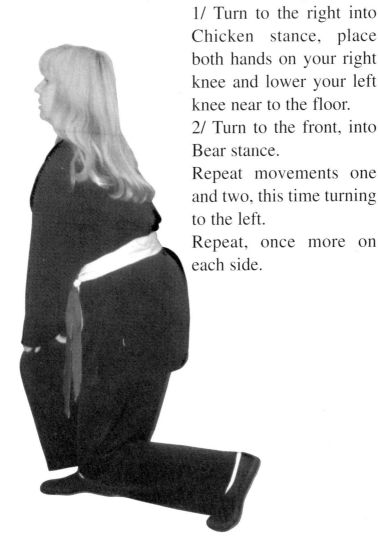

1/ Turn to the right into Chicken stance, place both hands on your right knee and lower your left knee near to the floor.

2/ Turn to the front, into Bear stance.

Repeat movements one and two, this time turning to the left.

Repeat, once more on each side.

Monkey (warm up exercise)

Stand in Right Monkey stance (left knee bent, right leg straight with your toes raised).

1/ Place both hands on your right knee and press gently three times.

2/ Change to Left Monkey stance and repeat as above, on your left side.

Repeat, once more on each side.

Extended Monkey (warm up exercise)

Stand in Extended Right Monkey (left leg bent, right leg straight with the toes raised).

1/ Keeping your back straight, lower your weight further downwards without strain.

Repeat the above movement on the left side.

Extended Dragon (warm up exercise)

1/ From Extended Monkey, turn to the right into Extended Right Dragon stance (both hands on your right knee), turn the instep of your left foot over to face the floor.

(Please listen to your own body and do not strain)

2/ Turn to your left into Extended Left Dragon stance (both hands on your left knee), turn the instep of your right foot over to face the floor.

Ankle Roll
(warm up exercise)

Sit on the floor in Double Plough stance (both legs straight out in front of you, hands are placed flat on the floor behind you). You can also sit on a chair.

1/ Cross your right leg over your left leg, take hold of the toes of your right foot with your left hand and hold your right ankle with your right hand.

2/ Circle your foot away from you (four times).

3/ Change direction and circle your foot towards you (four times).

Repeat all three movements on the opposite side.

Knee Press
(warm up exercise)

Start in Double Plough stance (both legs straight out in front of you)

1/ Cross your right leg over your left leg, draw your right leg in towards your body (as far as possible without strain).

2/ With your right hand, gently press your right knee towards the floor (without strain).

Repeat both movements on the opposite side.

Lift and Stretch (warm up exercise)

Start in Double Plough stance (both legs straight out in front of you, hands behind you, palms resting on the floor).

1/ Lift your bottom off the ground.

2/ Lower yourself back down.

3/ Take your arms as far forward as possible (without strain).

4/ Return to the starting position.

Repeat all four movements three more times.

Gentle Stretch (warm up exercise)

Sit on the floor in Double Plough stance (both legs straight out in front of you, hands behind you, palms resting on the floor).

1/ Move your left leg behind you.

2/ Sweep your left hand forwards towards your right foot (repeat, four times).

Return to Double Plough stance.

Repeat both movements on the opposite side.

A Moment in Time
Breathing Exercise

Start in a sitting position either (on the floor or in chair) with your legs crossed.

A/ The left leg should be furthest away from you, if you are sat in a chair, cross your legs at the ankles.

B/ LADIES ONLY turn your left palm to face downwards, join the middle finger and thumb together, place right thumb through the circle you have made with your finger and thumb so that your right thumb locates in the centre of your left palm. Now let your hands rest in your lap.

C/ GENTLEMEN ONLY turn your left palm to face upwards, join the middle finger and thumb together. Place the thumb of your right hand in the centre of your left palm. Now let your hands rest in your lap.

D/ LADIES and GENTLEMEN breathe in through the nose as you sink your breath as low as possible, allowing your stomach to expand (do not worry if you find it difficult to sink your breath at first, this will come with practise).

E/ Breathe out through the mouth as you allow your stomach to contract.

Try to think purely of the breath flowing into the body (via the nose) and out of the mouth. When you find other thoughts crowding in, simply return your thoughts once more to your breath. This exercise should be practised for a maximum of five minutes.

Heels Down
(warm up exercise)

Stand up and gently kick your heels straight down to the floor this helps to release any tension in the legs after sitting down.

Keeping the Joints Mobile (Hands and Arms 1)

A/ Turn your right palm face upwards (fingertips pointing forwards).

B/ Place the fingers of your left hand across the top of the fingers of your right hand (so that they are pointing to the right).

C/ Raise your right hand up into the air and straighten your elbow.

D/ Now lower your arm down.

Repeat A – D three more times.

Repeat A – D on the opposite side.

Keeping the Joints Mobile (Hands and Wrists 2)

A/ Place your right hand in front of your chest palm facing away from you, (fingertips pointing to the left).
B/ Now bend your wrist (pointing your fingertips

forwards) Your palm now faces to the right.
C/ Place the thumb of your left hand on top of your right hand and curl the fingers of your left hand underneath your right hand.
D/ Gently move your left and right hands upwards towards your nose.
E/ Gently move your left and right hands downwards.
Repeat D – E three more times.
Repeat all of the above on the opposite side.

Keeping the Joints Mobile (Hands and Wrists 3)

A/ Your right palm is facing towards you (fingertips pointing to the ceiling).

B/ Place the thumb of your left hand in the centre of the back of your right hand (thumbnail pointing towards the ceiling), and curl the fingers round the base of your right thumb.

C/ Gently push with your left thumb and pull with the fingers of your left hand (turning your right hand to your right).

D/ Allow the hands to return to the starting position.

Repeat C – D three more times.

Repeat all of the above on the opposite side.

Keeping the Joints Mobile (Hands and Wrists 4)

A/ Tuck your right elbow into your waist.

B/ Allow your right hand to flop down.

C/ Place your left hand across the top of the knuckles of your right hand.

D/ Apply a little pressure with your left hand (pressing downwards)

E/ Release the pressure.

Repeat D – E three more times.

Repeat all of the above on the opposite side.

Four Directional Breathing Exercise

Start in Riding Horse stance (both knees bent, both hands resting on your thighs).

A/ Breathe in through the nose as you draw both hands up in front of your chest and turn them so that the palms are facing away from you).

B.

D.

B/ Breathe out through the mouth as you push strongly forwards with both hands.

C/ Breathe in through the nose as you relax both arms and allow your hands to come back to your chest (palms facing you).

D/ Breathe out through the mouth as you push both arms out strongly sideways (palms facing away from you).

E/ Breathe in through the nose as you relax your arms and allow your hands to come back to

palms facing you).

F/ Breathe out through the mouth as you push both arms strongly upwards (palms facing upwards).

G/ Breathe in though the nose as you relax your arms and allow your hands to come back to your chest (palms facing you).

H/ Breathe out through the mouth as you push both arms strongly downwards (palms also facing downwards.

Repeat movements A – H once more.

Your warm up is now complete.

F.

H.

LFA T'ai Chi Sword Set

The LFA T'ai Chi Sword Set is made up of a sequence of soft flowing movements designed to improve the quality of your health, balance, co-ordination and concentration. As with all of the movements practised within the LFA, your personal progress does not relate to the quantity of movements you know, it relates to the quality of the movements which you practise.

It is important to incorporate the Taoist Walk into your movements (see the section on the Taoist Walk), this helps to ensure that there is no strain on the body.

We normally practise our T'ai Chi Sword set using a wooden double edged T'ai Chi Sword. The Swords are available to purchase from your class instructor or via our Website.

If you have difficulty maintaining your balance, do not use the stances which require you to stand on one leg, merely rest the ball of your foot on the ground (Cat stance). Most of all, your practise should be enjoyable, I personally have found that the Sword set is the easiest to learn, the difficult part came when I had to slow the movements down to the same speed as the T'ai Chi Form set.

Our T'ai Chi Sword set consist of 216 movements, the first 108 movements are practised slowly. The next 108 move like the wind.

If you are new to regular exercise, practise only a few movements at a time. Gradually, your stamina will improve and you will be able to practise for longer.

The advantage of practising LFA T'ai Chi over other types of exercise is that not only does it exercise the physical body, it also works on the internal parts of the body, helping to keep all of your organs healthy. At the same time, we use special breathing techniques to improve the functioning of your lungs; in addition your memory is also exercised. T'ai Chi is known as the Supreme Ultimate, it gives the mind, body and spirit a complete work out, without strain.

There is a saying in the West. "If you don't use it you lose it", our answer to this is "Practise LFA T'ai Chi to keep every part of you in good working order".

I am frequently asked how often people should practise, there is no one answer, we are all different. However, the more you put into LFA T'ai Chi, the more you will get out of it. For example a person who attends one class a week and does not practise until the next class will not receive the same benefit as the person who practises a little every day.

The beauty of LFA T'ai Chi is that it takes only a few minutes to practise the movements you need, yet the rewards are multiplied one hundred fold.

LFA T'ai Chi Stances

Although you may be eager to press on and learn the beneficial movements of our Sword set, it is important that you take the time to familiarise yourself with our stances.

First become familiar with their names, next check the position of your feet. It is important that you have the correct weight distribution without any strain on your body. If you attend a weekly class, your instructor will be able to advise you. However if you are unable to attend classes, I suggest you stand in front of a mirror to help you to achieve a good posture.

It is important to remember that our feet provide our roots, without which we fall over. Take the time to move from one stance to another while applying the Taoist Walk, only in this way will you reap the full benefits which are on offer to everyone.

In these early stages of your training, try and feel what is happening to the muscles of your body as you move slowly from one position to the next. Later on you will appreciate a far greater depth to the movements which you are practising. It is the person who takes their time and learns patience that will eventually achieve far more benefit than the person who rushes on claiming to know all the movements of the Sword set, (without really knowing them at all). Judging your progress by numbers is very much a Western concept, the LFA are purely interested in improving the quality of your life. There is no time limit, or pressure applied to your learning. Enjoy your practise, and find the path to a different way of living.

Bear Stance

Bear stance is achieved by standing with your feet shoulder width apart. Your body should be relaxed with no tension. Both of your arms should be hanging loosely by your sides. You should be looking straight ahead.

We use Bear stance at the beginning of all of our sets, when we adopt the 'Prepare' position.

Cat Stance

To achieve a Right Cat stance, the left leg is bent at the knee, the heel is raised on your right foot. The ball of the right foot rests lightly on the floor with eighty percent of your weight on your left leg.

To achieve Left Cat stance, the right leg is bent at the knee, the heel is raised on your left foot. The ball of the left foot rests lightly on the floor with eighty percent of your weight on your right leg.

Crane Stance

To achieve a Right Crane stance move your weight onto your left leg (bending your left knee slightly to aid your balance). At the same time raise your right leg (bending your right knee) until your thigh is parallel

with the floor. Students who have difficulty balancing should use a Cat stance for movements which require one leg to be lifted off the floor.

To achieve a Left Crane stance take your weight onto your right leg (bending your right knee slightly to aid your balance). At the same time raise your left leg (bending your left knee) until your thigh is parallel with the floor.

Crossed Legs Stance

To achieve Right Crossed Legs stance, bend your left knee slightly. Now cross your right leg in front of and slightly beyond your left leg, raise the heel of your right foot.

To achieve Left Crossed Legs stance, bend your right knee slightly. Now cross your left leg in front of and slightly beyond your right leg, raise the heel of your left foot.

Dog Stance

To achieve Right Dog stance, take your weight onto  your left leg (bending the knee slightly to aid your balance). At the same time extend and raise your right leg forwards, your leg should be at a height which is comfortable to you without strain. To achieve Left Dog stance, take your weight onto your right leg (bending the knee slightly to aid your balance). At the same time extend and raise your left leg forwards.

Dragon Stance

To achieve a Right Dragon stance step forwards from either a Bear or an Eagle stance. It is important not to over step, make sure you have a good gap (width ways) between your feet.

Drift your weight over to your right side, so that the weight is spread between your right hip, knee and ankle. Eighty percent of your weight should be on your right leg, your left leg should be straight although not locked.

To achieve a Left Dragon stance, follow the same procedure as above this time stepping forward with your left leg.

Duck Stance

To achieve a Right Duck stance from Eagle stance, step behind with your left foot, placing your heel down first. Now drift your weight onto your left leg

(bending your knee), your right leg should be straight, although not locked.

To achieve a Left Duck stance from Eagle stance, step back with your right foot, placing your heel down first. Now drift your weight onto your right leg (bending your knee), your left leg should be straight, although not locked.

Eagle Stance

Eagle stance is achieved by placing both heels together, toes pointing slightly outwards. Your weight should be evenly balanced between both legs. Your body should be relaxed with your arms by your sides.

Leopard Stance

To achieve a Right Leopard stance take a pace off sideways to your right (bending your right knee and drifting your weight across). At the same time straighten your left leg.

To achieve a Left Leopard stance take a pace off sideways to your left (bending your left knee and drifting your weight across). At the same time straighten your right leg.

Monkey Stance

To achieve a Right Monkey stance step back with your left leg (bending your left knee). Your right leg is straight with the toes of your right foot raised.

To achieve a Left Monkey stance step back with your right leg (bending your right knee). Your left leg is straight with the toes of your left foot raised.

Praying Mantis Stance

To achieve Praying Mantis stance, kneel down on both knees and sit on your feet.

Scissors Stance

To achieve a Right Scissors stance drift your weight onto your left leg (bending your knee slightly). Now cross your right leg behind and slightly beyond your left leg, raising the heel of your right foot.

To achieve a Left Scissors stance drift your weight onto your right leg (bending your knee slightly). Now cross your left leg behind and slightly beyond your right leg, raising the heel of your left foot.

Snake Stance

To achieve a Right Snake stance take a small pace forwards with your right leg. Both knees are slightly bent, your weight is evenly distributed between both legs.

To achieve a Left Snake stance take a small pace forwards with your left leg. Both knees are slightly bent, your weight is evenly distributed between both legs.

Chicken Stance

To achieve a right Chicken stance turn ninety degrees to the right. Your right leg is in front of your left leg. Bend both knees, your left knee lowers to just above the ground (see photograph). Repeat on the left side to achieve a left Chicken stance.

List of Stances 1 – 108

1	Eagle
2	Right Snake
3	Left Dragon
4	Right Dog
5	Right Leopard
6	Left Crane
7	Right Dragon
8	Left Scissors
9	Left Stork
10	Left Dragon
11	Right Dog
12	Right Dragon
13	Left Leopard
14	Left Dragon
15	Left Dragon
16	Right Cat
17	Left Crane
18	Left Leopard
19	Right Leopard
20	Left Dragon
21	Right Cat
22	Left Dragon
23	Right Dragon
24	Left Leopard

25	Right Scissors
26	Bear
27	Right Scissors
28	Left Dragon
29	Right Dog
30	Left Duck
31	Right Leopard
32	Left Dragon
33	Right Cat
34	Left Cat
35	Left Dragon
36	Left Dog
37	Left Dragon
38	Right Dragon
39	Right Duck
40	Right Scissors
41	Right Leopard
42	Left Crane
43	Right Dragon
44	Left Scissors
45	Left Stork
46	Left Dragon
47	Right Dog
48	Right Dragon
49	Right Leopard

50	Eagle
51	Right Dragon
52	Right Scissors
53	Left Leopard
54	Left Crane
55	Left Hawk
56	Right Chicken
57	Left Dragon
58	Right Dragon
59	Right Dragon
60	Left Cat
61	Left Stork
62	Right Duck
63	Right Scissors
64	Left Leopard
65	Right Crane
66	Left Dragon
67	Left Duck
68	Right Duck
69	Right Scissors
70	Left Leopard
71	Left Dragon
72	Right Crane
73	Left Duck
74	Right Dragon

75	Right Scissors
76	Right Duck
77	Left Duck
78	Right Scissors
79	Left Scissors
80	Right Stork
81	Right Leopard
82	Left Hawk
83	Left Stork
84	Right Duck
85	Right Leopard
86	Right Stork
87	Right Dragon
88	Right Hawk
89	Right Dragon
90	Right Leopard
91	Right Scissors
92	Right Stork
93	Right Dragon
94	Right Leopard
95	Left Duck
96	Right Dragon
97	Left Stork
98	Right Dragon
99	Left Duck

The LFA T'ai Chi Sword Set

Movements 1 to 108

LFA T'AI CHI SWORD

Starting Position

Stand in Eagle stance both heels together, toes pointing slightly outwards. Your weight is evenly distributed between both legs.

Your sword is held in your left hand, the blade points upwards behind your arm. Your left index finger is pointing down the handle of your sword (see photograph). Your right arm is by your right side.

Prepare

From Eagle stance take a pace out sideways with your left foot into Bear stance. Remember, always place your heel down first when practising LFA T'ai Chi.

Your sword remains in your left hand.

Number 1

From Bear stance draw your left foot back to your right foot into Eagle stance (heels together, toes pointing slightly outwards.

Your sword remains in the same position as it was in for 'Prepare'.

Number 2

From Eagle stance step forwards with your right foot into Right Snake stance (both knees slightly bent, weight evenly distributed between both legs).

At the same time circle your left hand round in front of your body (waist height). Now hold the sword handle in your right hand by covering the index finger of your left hand with your right hand. Once your right hand is holding the sword, the fingertips of your left hand move and point towards the blade of your sword (see photograph).

Number 3

From Right Snake stance step forward into Left Dragon stance. Remember to apply the principles of the Taoist Walk.

At the same time your sword sweeps slightly forwards and upwards. Your left hand moves with the momentum of your sword, the fingertips are still pointing towards the blade (see photograph).

Number 4

From Left Dragon stance swing your right leg forward into Right Dog stance. Your left knee is bent to aid your balance.

At the same time your sword sweeps slightly forwards and upwards. Your left hand follows the momentum of your sword (the fingertips of your left hand continue to point to the blade).

Number 5

From Right Dog stance turn ninety degrees to your right into Right Leopard stance, this is achieved by swinging your right leg behind you and turning your right foot to the right as you place your right heel down. Now transfer your weight onto your right leg and pivot on the heel of your left foot (your right leg should be bent and your left leg should be straight).

At the same time your sword sweeps over to the right, moving downwards then upwards to finish as shown in the photograph, (your right palm is facing away from you), you are looking along the blade of your sword. Your left hand follows the movement of your sword to finish with the fingertips pointing towards the blade.

Number 6

From Right Leopard stance raise your left leg into Left Crane stance (left knee bent, thigh parallel to the floor).

At the same time the blade of your sword turns over as you lower your right elbow into your waist, (your right palm is facing to the left). Your left elbow moves to finish at the left side of your waist with the palm of your left hand facing to the right (fingertips pointing forwards).

Number 7

From Left Crane stance place your left foot flat on the floor, now raise your right leg into Right Crane stance, then move it forwards to finish in Right Dragon stance. Remember to place your heel down first. Your sword remains in the same position as it was in for movement number six.

Number 8

From Right Dragon stance turn ninety degrees to your right into Left Scissors stance. This is achieved by drifting your weight onto your left leg, bend your left knee, now pivot on the heel of your right foot, bend your right knee and raise the heel on your left foot.

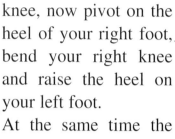

At the same time the blade of your sword turns over as you move your sword sideways to extend forwards at shoulder height (your right palm is facing away from you). Your left hand follows the momentum of the sword to finish with the fingertips of your left hand pointing towards the blade. You are looking along the blade of your sword.

Number 9

From Left Scissors stance raise your left leg into Left Stork stance (right knee bent to aid your balance).

At the same time your sword circles out to your left,

around the back of your left shoulder, to finish behind your right shoulder (the blade of your sword is pointing downwards). Your left hand extends forwards in front of your left shoulder (palm facing away from you, fingertips pointing to the ceiling)

Number 10

From Left Stork stance turn ninety degrees to the left into Left Dragon stance. Remember to apply the principles of the Taoist Walk.

At the same time your right arm (still holding your sword) circles out behind you and then round to finish underneath your left armpit. Your left arm extends forwards at shoulder height (palm facing away from you, fingertips pointing to the ceiling).

Number 11

From Left Dragon stance swing and raise your right leg forwards into Right Dog stance.

Your sword and hands remain in the same positions as they were in for movement number ten.

Number 12

From Right Dog stance step forwards into Right Dragon stance.

At the same time your sword sweeps forward and over to finish inclined with both hands on the sword (see photograph).

Number 13

From Right Dragon stance turn ninety degrees to your left into Left Leopard stance. This is achieved by first placing your left foot in position, then drifting your weight across to the left. Your left leg should be bent and your right leg should be straight. At the same time pull your left elbow across your body (also bending your right elbow). Your left elbow is bent pointing to the left, your right elbow points downwards. Your sword finishes at eye level with your left hand on top of your sword handle and your right hand underneath it.

Number 14

From Left Leopard stance turn ninety degrees to your left into Left Dragon stance. This is achieved by pivoting on the heel of your right foot, and then placing your weight onto your right leg. Now pick up your left foot and place it into position, drifting your weight across to your left leg.

At the same time let go of your sword with your left hand, your right arm circles over the top to finish extended forwards at shoulder height (still holding

your sword). Your left arm extends forwards at shoulder height (palm facing away from you, fingertips pointing to the ceiling).

Number 15

Stay in Left Dragon stance for movement fifteen.
At the same time (still holding your sword) your right arm sweeps downwards and to the rear (you are looking at your sword). Your left hand remains in the same position it was in for movement number fourteen.

Number 16

From Left Dragon stance step through with your right foot into Right Cat stance. The ball of your right foot should be resting lightly on the floor, your left knee should be bent.

At the same time your sword sweeps forward and up to finish with your right elbow level with the right side of your waist. Your left elbow bends to finish level with the left side of your waist (your left palm is facing to the right, with your fingertips pointing straight ahead).

Number 17

From Right Cat stance place your right heel on the floor and raise your left leg into Left Crane stance. Your sword and hands remain in the same positions as they were in for movement number sixteen.

Number 18

From Left Crane stance turn ninety degrees to the left into Left Leopard stance. This is achieved by first placing your left foot into position, then drifting your weight across onto your left leg and pivoting on the heel of your right foot (left knee bent, right leg straight, both feet are pointing forwards).

At the same time raise your sword, placing both hands on the handle. Pull your left elbow across your body, (the same as in movement number thirteen).

Number 19

From Left Leopard stance transfer your weight across to your right leg into Right Leopard stance (do not move your feet).

At the same time let go of your sword with your left hand. Now turn your sword over and pull your right elbow back so that it points to the right. Your left hand extends out sideways at shoulder height (palm facing away from you, fingertips pointing to the ceiling).

Number 20

From Right Leopard stance turn ninety degrees to the left into Left Dragon stance. This is achieved by picking up your left foot and placing it in position then correcting your right foot, heel and toe.

At the same time circle your right arm over the top and to the rear, to finish with your sword pointing to the floor. Your left arm extends forward at shoulder height (palm facing away from you, fingertips pointing to the ceiling).

Number 21

From Left Dragon stance step into Right Cat stance. Your left knee is bent and your right heel is raised.

At the same time your sword sweeps upwards in your right hand, to finish with your right elbow tucked into the right side of your waist. Your left elbow tucks into the left side of your waist (your left palm is facing to the right, fingertips pointing straight ahead.

Number 22

From Right Cat stance place your right heel flat on the floor and step through into Left Dragon stance. Remember to apply the Taoist Walk.

At the same time your left hand sweeps forwards and upwards to finish at head height (palm facing away from you, fingertips pointing to the right-see photograph). Your sword sweeps slightly upwards to finish pointing diagonally to the left.

Number 23

From Left Dragon stance step forward into Right Dragon stance. Remember to apply the principles of the Taoist Walk.

At the same time draw your left hand back near to your left ear (palm facing to the left, fingertips pointing forwards). Your sword extends forwards in your right hand at shoulder height.

Number 24

From Right Dragon stance turn ninety degrees to your left into Left Leopard stance. This is achieved by placing your left foot in position first, and then pivoting (heel and toe) on your right foot (left knee bent, right leg straight).

At the same time, take hold of your sword with both hands pulling your left elbow to the left, like movement number thirteen.

Number 25

From Left Leopard stance cross your right foot behind your left leg into Right Scissors stance (both knees bent, right heel raised).

At the same time let go of your sword with your left hand, your right arm crosses over your left arm so that your sword points downwards at the left side of your body. Your left hand finishes underneath your right arm (palm facing away from you, fingertips pointing towards the ceiling).

Number 26

From Right Scissors stance place your right heel flat on the floor and step sideways with your left foot into Bear stance (remember to place your heel down first).

At the same time your sword sweeps across your body (still pointing down-wards) before circling upwards and over to finish with the blade pointing to the left. Your left hand points to the blade of your sword (see photograph).

Number 27

From Bear stance cross your right foot behind your left leg into Right Scissors stance (both knees bent, right heel raised).

At the same time your sword circles down and to the right, (sword pointing down) then upwards across your body, to finish with your right arm underneath your left arm (the blade of your sword is now pointing upwards). Your left hand finishes in front of your right shoulder (palm facing inwards).

Number 28

From Right Scissors stance turn two hundred and seventy degrees to your right into Left Dragon stance. At the same time your sword sweeps round with the movement of your body, to finish with your right arm extended behind you (sword pointing to the floor). You should be looking at your sword. Your left arm extends forwards at shoulder height (palm facing away from you, fingertips pointing to the ceiling).

Number 29

From Left Dragon stance swing your right leg forwards and raise it into Right Dog stance.

At the same time hold your sword with both hands as you swing it upwards, (you should be looking at the blade of your sword). See photograph.

Number 30

From Right Dog stance step behind with your right foot into Left Duck stance (remember to place your right heel down first).

At the same time your sword sweeps downwards to finish angled upwards from your body (see photograph).

Number 31

From Left Duck stance turn ninety degrees to your left into Right Leopard stance. This is achieved by first pivoting on the heel of your left foot.

At the same time let go of your sword with your left hand. Now turn your sword over to finish with the blade flat, (pointing to the left) at shoulder height in front of your body. Your left arm also finishes in front of your body.

Note: the front view is shown but the actual position is with the back to the camera.

Number 32

From Right Leopard stance turn ninety degrees to the left into Left Dragon stance.

At the same time your sword sweeps over the top to the rear, finishing with your sword pointing to the floor, (you should be looking at your sword). Your left hand finishes extended forward at shoulder height (palm facing away from you, fingertips pointing to the ceiling). This movement is the same as movement number twenty.

Number 33

From Left Dragon stance step through into Right Cat stance (left knee bent, heel raised on your right foot).

At the same time your sword sweeps upwards to finish extended forward at waist height. Your left elbow tucks into the left side of your waist (palm facing to the right, fingertips pointing straight ahead). This movement is the same as movement number twentyone.

Number 34

From Right Cat stance place your right heel flat on the floor, bend your right knee and raise your left heel into Left Cat stance.

At the same time take hold of your sword with both hands and move the blade so that your sword is pointing straight upwards.

Number 35

From Left Cat stance step forward into Left Dragon stance.

At the same time let go of your sword with your left hand and extend your sword forward at shoulder height. Your left hand moves to guard your right elbow.

Number 36

From Left Dragon stance raise your left leg into Left Dog stance (right knee bent to aid your balance).

At the same time draw your sword back into a right archer (right hand near to your right ear). Your left hand extends forward at shoulder height (palm facing away from you, fingertips pointing to the ceiling).

Number 37

From Left Dog stance lower your left leg into Left Dragon stance. Remember to apply the principles of the Taoist Walk.

At the same time take hold of your sword with both hands as it extends forward at shoulder height.

Number 38

From Left Dragon stance turn one hundred and eighty degrees to your right into Right Dragon stance. Remember to apply the Taoist Walk.

At the same your sword circles over the top as you make your turn, to finish extended forward at shoulder height.

Number 39

From Right Dragon stance drift your weight back into Right Duck stance (left knee bent, right leg straight). At the same time your sword moves back to finish angled upwards from the centre of your body.

Number 40

From Right Duck stance cross your right foot behind your left leg into Right Scissors stance (both knees bent, right heel raised).

At the same time your right arm crosses over your left arm (both elbows pointing upwards) your sword is pointing downwards at your left side.

Number 41

From Right Scissors stance step sideways with your right foot into Right Leopard stance (your right knee is bent, your left leg is straight).

At the same time your sword sweeps over, down and up to finish in the same position as movement number five. Your left hand points to the blade of your sword.

Number 42

From Right Leopard stance raise your left leg into Left Crane stance (your left knee is bent with your thigh parallel to the floor).

At the same time your right elbow tucks into the right side of your waist, your sword is extended forward at waist height. Your left elbow tucks into the left side of your waist. This movement is the same as movement number six.

Number 43

From Left Crane stance step through into Right Dragon stance. This is achieved by first placing your left foot on the floor then raising your right leg into Right Crane stance, then placing your right heel down and moving your weight forwards into your Right Dragon stance.

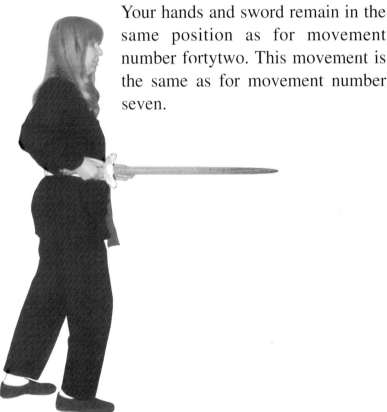

Your hands and sword remain in the same position as for movement number fortytwo. This movement is the same as for movement number seven.

Number 44

From Right Dragon stance turn ninety degrees to the right into Left Scissors stance (both knees bent, your right heel is raised).

At the same time the blade of your sword turns over to finish at eye level. Your left hand is pointing to the blade of your sword. This movement is the same as movement number eight.

Number 45

From Left Scissors stance raise your left leg up into Left Stork stance with your left leg wrapped around your right leg (bend your right leg to aid your balance).

At the same time your sword circles to the left, moving around the back of your head to finish behind your right shoulder (blade pointing downwards). Your left hand finishes in front of your left shoulder (palm facing away from you, fingertips pointing to the ceiling). This movement is the same as movement number nine.

Number 46

From Left Stork stance turn ninety degrees to your left into Left Dragon stance.

At the same time your sword circles forward and to the left to finish u n d e r n e a t h your left arm (with the blade pointing to the rear). Your left arm extends forward at shoulder height (palm facing away from you, f i n g e r t i p s pointing to the ceiling). This movement is the same as for m o v e m e n t number ten.

Number 47

From Left Dragon stance raise your right leg into Right Dog stance (bend your left knee to aid your balance).

Your sword and hands remain in the same position as for movement number fortysix. This movement is the same as movement number eleven.

Number 48

From Right Dog stance lower your right leg into Right Dragon stance.

At the same time sweep your sword upwards, taking hold of it with both hands. This movement is the same as movement number twelve.

Number 49

From Right Dragon stance turn ninety degrees to the right into Right Leopard stance (your right knee is bent and your left leg is straight).

At the same time let go of your sword with your left hand. Now draw your right elbow back to your right (see photograph), your sword finishes at eye level. Your left arm extends forward at shoulder height (palm facing away from you, fingertips pointing to the ceiling). This movement finishes in the same position as movement number nineteen although you are facing in the opposite direction.

Number 50

From Right Leopard stance draw your left foot into Eagle stance (both heels together, toes pointing slightly outwards).

At the same time circle your sword to your right then downwards in front of your body. Now transfer your sword from your right hand to your left hand. You should once more be back in the starting position, with your sword behind your left arm. Your right arm rests by your right side.

Number 51

From Eagle stance step forty five degrees to the right (diagonally) into Right Dragon stance.

At the same time transfer your sword from your left hand to your right hand. Your sword sweeps up to shoulder height (see photograph), the fingertips of your left hand point to the centre of your sword.

Number 52

From Right Dragon stance, turn fortyfive degrees to your left (to face the front). Your right leg crosses behind and slightly beyond your left leg into Right Scissors stance. At the same time your right arm moves by your right side, still holding the sword (palm facing forwards). Your sword is angled down to the floor. Your left hand moves to cover your right shoulder.

Number 53

From Right Scissors stance, place your right heel down and step sideways into Left Leopard stance (left knee bent, right leg straight).
At the same time raise your sword in your right hand to eye level. Now place your left hand on top of your sword (palm facing down, fingertips pointing to the right). Draw your left elbow to the left (you are looking along the blade of your sword). See photograph

Number 54

From Left Leopard stance turn ninety degrees to the right into Left Crane stance. This is achieved by pivoting on the heel of your right foot. Raise and bend your left knee until your left thigh is parallel to the floor.

At the same time point the blade of your sword upwards (both hands holding the sword).

Number 55

From Left Crane stance, extend your left leg out directly behind you into Left Hawk stance. Bend your right leg slightly to help your balance.

At the same time your sword points directly forwards from your solar plexus.

Number 56

From Left Hawk stance, lower your left leg into Right Chicken stance (do not strain).

Your sword remains in the same position as it was in for movement number fiftyfive.

Number 57

From Right Chicken stance, step through into Left Dragon stance. Remember to apply the principles of the Taoist Walk.

At the same time your right arm is pulled back to your right ear (still holding the sword), your left hand is extended forward, fingertips pointing to the ceiling.

Number 58

From Left Dragon stance turn one hundred and eighty degrees to your right into Right Dragon stance. Remember to apply the principles of the Taoist Walk. At the same time as you make your turn, your sword travels over the top. Your left hand extends forwards, fingertips are pointing to the ceiling.

Number 59

Stay in Right Dragon stance for movement number fifty nine.

At the same time your left arm remains at shoulder height (palm facing away from you, fingertips pointing to the ceiling). Your right arm swings out behind you while still holding your sword. You are looking at your sword (behind you).

Number 60

From Right Dragon stance, step into Left Cat stance (heel raised on your left foot).

At the same time allow your sword to sweep forwards and upwards until your right elbow is against your waist (the arm movements are like movement number sixteen). Your left elbow finishes at the left side of your waist, (palm facing to the right, fingertips pointing forwards).

Number 61

From Left Cat stance, bend your left knee and raise your left leg into Left Stork stance. Bend your right knee slightly to help your balance.

At the same time raise your right arm to eye level, the blade of your sword is pointing to the left. The finger tips of your left hand point to the blade of your sword (see photograph).

Number 62

From Left Stork stance turn ninety degrees to your left into Right Duck stance (this is not the usual Duck stance i.e. your right foot does not move, your left foot turns ninety degrees to the left (drift your weight onto your left leg).

At the same time your right arm is positioned by your right side with your sword pointing to the floor (see photograph). Draw your left hand back near to your left ear (palm facing to the left).

Number 63

From Right Duck stance, cross your right foot behind your left into Right Scissors stance (the heel is raised on your right foot.

At the same time raise your sword to eye level, now place your left hand on top of your sword. Move your left elbow out to the left (see photograph).

Number 64

From Right Scissors stance, place your right heel flat on the floor and step sideways into Left Leopard stance (left leg bent, right leg straight).

At the same time allow your right hand (which is holding your sword) to swing over to the right, to finish with your sword pointing down to the floor. Your left hand moves to cover your right shoulder, (palm facing towards you).

Number 65

From Leopard stance, raise your right leg into Right Crane stance. Bend your left knee slightly to help your balance.

At the same time raise your sword level with your forehead (blade pointing to the left). The fingertips of your left hand are pointing to the blade of your sword (see photograph).

Number 66

From Right Crane stance, turn ninety degrees to your left into Left Dragon stance.

At the same time place both hands on your sword as it moves over with the turn of your body.

Number 67

From Left Dragon stance, drift your weight back onto your right leg into Left Duck stance (right leg bent, left leg straight).

At the same time draw both hands (still holding your sword) back to your solar plexus (see photograph).

Number 68

From Left Duck stance, step back with your left foot into Right Duck stance (placing your left heel down first).

At the same time let go of your sword with your left hand and draw your left hand back near to your left ear, (palm facing to the left). Your right arm extends forwards (still holding your sword).

Number 69

From Right Duck stance, cross your right leg behind your left into Right Scissors stance (heel raised on your right foot).

At the same time draw your sword back so that it is at eye level (both hands are on the sword), the blade of your sword is pointing to the right (the arm movements are like movement number thirteen).

Number 70

From Right Scissors stance, place your right heel flat on the floor and step sideways (to the left) into Left Leopard stance (left leg bent, right leg straight).

At the same time let go of your sword with your left hand and place your left hand in front of your right shoulder (palm facing towards you). Your right hand (still holding the sword) swings down to the right hand side of your body (the blade of your sword is pointing down to the floor).

Number 71

From Left Leopard stance turn ninety degrees to the left into Left Dragon Stance. Remember to apply the principles of the Taoist Walk.

At the same time your sword sweeps under and upwards as you turn to the left. Both hands are on the sword (see photograph).

Number 72

From Left Dragon stance, raise your right leg into Right Crane stance (thigh parallel to the floor).

At the same (still holding your sword in both hands), move the blade so that it is in the same position as movement number thirtyfour (see photograph).

Number 73

From Right Crane stance, step behind with your right leg (placing your heel down first) into Left Duck stance.

At the same time let go of your sword with your left hand and allow it to extend forwards at shoulder height (palm facing away from you, fingertips pointing to the ceiling). Draw your right hand back near to your right ear (still holding the sword).

Number 74

From Left Duck stance, turn one hundred and eighty degrees to your right into Right Dragon stance.

At the same time (as you turn), your left hand returns to the sword. Your sword moves over the top to finish extended forwards (see photograph).

Number 75

From Right Dragon stance, turn ninety degrees to the left into Right Scissors stance (the heel is raised on your right foot).

At the same time move the sword into the same position as movement number thirteen.

Number 76

From Right Scissors stance, place your right heel down on the floor and step forty five degrees to the right (diagonally) into Right Duck stance.

At the same time lower both hands down so that your sword extends forward from your solar plexus.

Number 77

From Right Duck stance, step behind into Left Duck stance (still on the diagonal).

At the same time lower both hands down so that your sword is pointing down to the floor (see photograph).

Number 78

From Left Duck stance turn fortyfive degrees to your left into Right Scissors stance (you are now facing the front).

At the same time your sword circles to the left, then up and over to the right, finishing with it pointing down to the floor by your right side.

Number 79

From Right Scissors stance, place your right heel down on the floor and take your left foot behind your right, into Left Scissors stance.

At the same time your sword circles back over to the left hand side of your body. Your sword finishes pointing down to the floor at the left hand side of your body.

Number 80

From Left Scissors stance, place your left heel flat on the floor and raise your right leg into Right Stork stance.

At the same time, simply raise both hands up (as shown in the photograph) so that the sword points down from your left shoulder.

Number 81

From Right Stork stance step sideways into Right Leopard stance (right knee bent, left leg straight).

At the same time your sword lowers down to the left side of your body (both hands are holding the handle of your sword).

Number 82

From Right Leopard stance turn ninety degrees to your right into Left Hawk stance (bend your right knee to aid your balance).

At the same time your sword moves to extend forward from your solar plexus.

Number 83

From Left Hawk stance straighten your body vertically into Left Stork stance (with your left leg wrapped around your right leg).

Your sword moves to point v e r t i c a l l y upwards.

Number 84

From Left Stork stance step behind with your left foot into Right Duck stance (remember to place your left heel down first).

At the same time lower your sword down to extend forward at waist height.

Number 85

From Right Duck stance turn ninety degrees to the right into Right Leopard stance (your right knee is bent and your left leg is straight).

At the same time pull your sword back (in your right hand) into a right archer (near to your right ear). Your left hand extends sideways at shoulder height.

Number 86

From Right Leopard stance drift your weight across to your left and raise your right leg into a Right Stork stance.

Your sword remains in the same position as it was in for movement number eightyfive.

Number 87

From Right Stork stance turn ninety degrees to your right into Right Dragon stance.

At the same time draw your left hand back into a left archer (near to your left ear). Your sword extends forward at shoulder height.

Number 88

From Right Dragon stance move your right leg out to the rear into a Right Hawk stance (bend your left leg to aid your balance).

At the same time swing your sword behind you, your left arm extends forward at shoulder height (palm facing away from you, fingertips pointing to the ceiling). You should be looking behind you, at your sword.

Number 89

From Right Hawk stance turn one hundred and eighty degrees to your right into Right Dragon stance.

At the same time take hold of your sword with both hands. Your sword circles over the top as you make your turn, finishing angled upwards from your solar plexus.

Number 90

From Right Dragon turn ninety degrees to your right into Right Leopard stance (your right leg is bent and your left leg is straight).

At the same time your right arm crosses over your left, (your sword is pointing down to the floor at the left hand side of your body). Your left hand is underneath your right arm. This is the same finishing position as movement number twentyfive.

Number 91

From Right Leopard stance move your right leg behind your left leg into Right Scissors stance (both knees bent, the heel is raised on your right foot).

At the same time your sword circles over the top to the right hand side of your body (your sword is pointing down to the floor). Your left hand draws back into a left archer (near to your left ear).

Number 92

From Right Scissors stance raise your right leg into Right Stork stance (bend your left knee to aid your balance).

At the same time take hold of your sword with both hands, raise it to eye level with the blade pointing to the right (see photograph).

Number 93

From Right Stork stance turn ninety degrees to your right into Right Dragon stance. Remember to apply the principles of the Taoist walk.

At the same time let go of your sword with your left hand. Your sword extends forward at shoulder height. Your left hand draws back into a left archer (near to your left ear).

Number 94

From Right Dragon stance turn ninety degrees to the right into Right Leopard stance (right leg bent, left leg straight).

At the same time take hold of your sword with both hands. Your sword finishes pointing down to the floor at the left hand side of your body.

Number 95

From Right Leopard stance step behind with your right foot into Left Duck stance (remember to place your right heel down first).

At the same time circle your sword up and over to finish with it extended f o r w a r d from your solar plexus (both hands are still on your sword).

Number 96

From Left Duck stance turn ninety degrees to your right into Right Dragon stance. Remember to apply the principles of the Taoist walk.

At the same time let go of your sword with your left hand. Your right hand circles over the top, your sword finishes pointing down to the floor, behind you. Your left arm extends forward at shoulder height (palm facing away from you, fingertips pointing to the ceiling). The arm positions are the same as for movement number twenty.

Number 97

From Right Dragon stance raise and wrap your left leg around the back of your right leg into Left Stork stance.

At the same time circle your sword over to finish at eye level with your sword pointing to the left. Your left hand is pointing to the blade of your sword.

Number 98

From Left stork stance turn ninety degrees to your left into Right Dragon stance. Remember to apply the principles of the Taoist walk.

At the same time draw your left hand back into a left archer (near to your left ear). Your sword is extended forward at shoulder height.

Number 99

From Right Dragon stance step behind with your right foot into Left Duck stance (remember to place your right heel down first).

At the same time take hold of your sword with both hands, extending it forwards from your solar plexus.

Number 100

From Left Duck stance move your weight forward into Left Dragon stance. Remember to apply the principles of the Taoist walk.

Your sword remains in the same position as it was in for movement number ninetynine.

Number 101

From Left Dragon stance lower your weight down into Left Chicken stance (please be careful not to strain when practising this movement).

Your sword remains in the same position as it was in for movement number one hundred.

Number 102

From Left Chicken stance lower both knees down into Praying Mantis.

At the same time your sword points vertically upwards.

Number 103

From Praying Mantis stance stand up into Right Leopard stance (right leg bent, left leg straight).

At the same time lower your sword down to the left hand side of your body.

Number 104

From Right Leopard stance raise your right leg into Right Crane stance.

At the same time let go of your sword with your left hand. Now circle your sword to the right, then over to finish at eye level with your sword pointing to the left. Your left hand is pointing to your sword.

Number 105

From Right Crane stance cross your left foot behind your right leg into Left Scissors stance (both knees are bent, the heel is raised on your left foot).

At the same time your sword circles over to the right hand side of your body (you are holding the sword with both hands).

Number 106

From Left Scissors stance place your left foot next to your right foot into Eagle stance (both heels together, toes pointing slightly outwards).

Your sword remains in the same position as it was in for movement number one hundred and five.

Number 107

Stay in Eagle stance for movement one hundred and seven.

At the same time your sword circles over to the left hand side of your body.

Number 108

From Eagle stance step sideways with your left foot into Bear stance (feet shoulder width apart).

At the same time let go of your sword with your left hand and circle it to the right and over, to finish at head height with it pointing to the left. Your left hand points to the blade of your sword.

LFA T'AI CHI SWORD

The LFA T'ai Chi Sword Set is for everyone. This book is more than a beginners' guide because in addition to teaching the first 108 movements of our Sword set, it contains a compendium of important information as follows: The Chang Ming health diet; the essence of LFA T'ai Chi; the Way of Occlusion and the warm up exercises which we use in our classes. To find the inner depth within the movements, you may wish to train with us at our ever-growing number of LFA classes and day courses as shown on our Website www.leefamilyarts.com

I hope you have enjoyed learning the first one hundred and eight movements of our Sword Set (which is the easiest Set to learn).

We intend to publish the remainder of the movements in a subsequent book in the not too distant future. May you continue to enjoy your journey with the Lee Family Arts and the LFA.

LFA T'AI CHI SWORD

Notes

Notes

LFA T'AI CHI SWORD

Notes

LFA T'AI CHI SWORD

Notes

LFA T'AI CHI SWORD

Notes

LFA T'AI CHI SWORD

Notes

LFA T'AI CHI SWORD

Notes